THE UNSINKABLE

Walker Bean

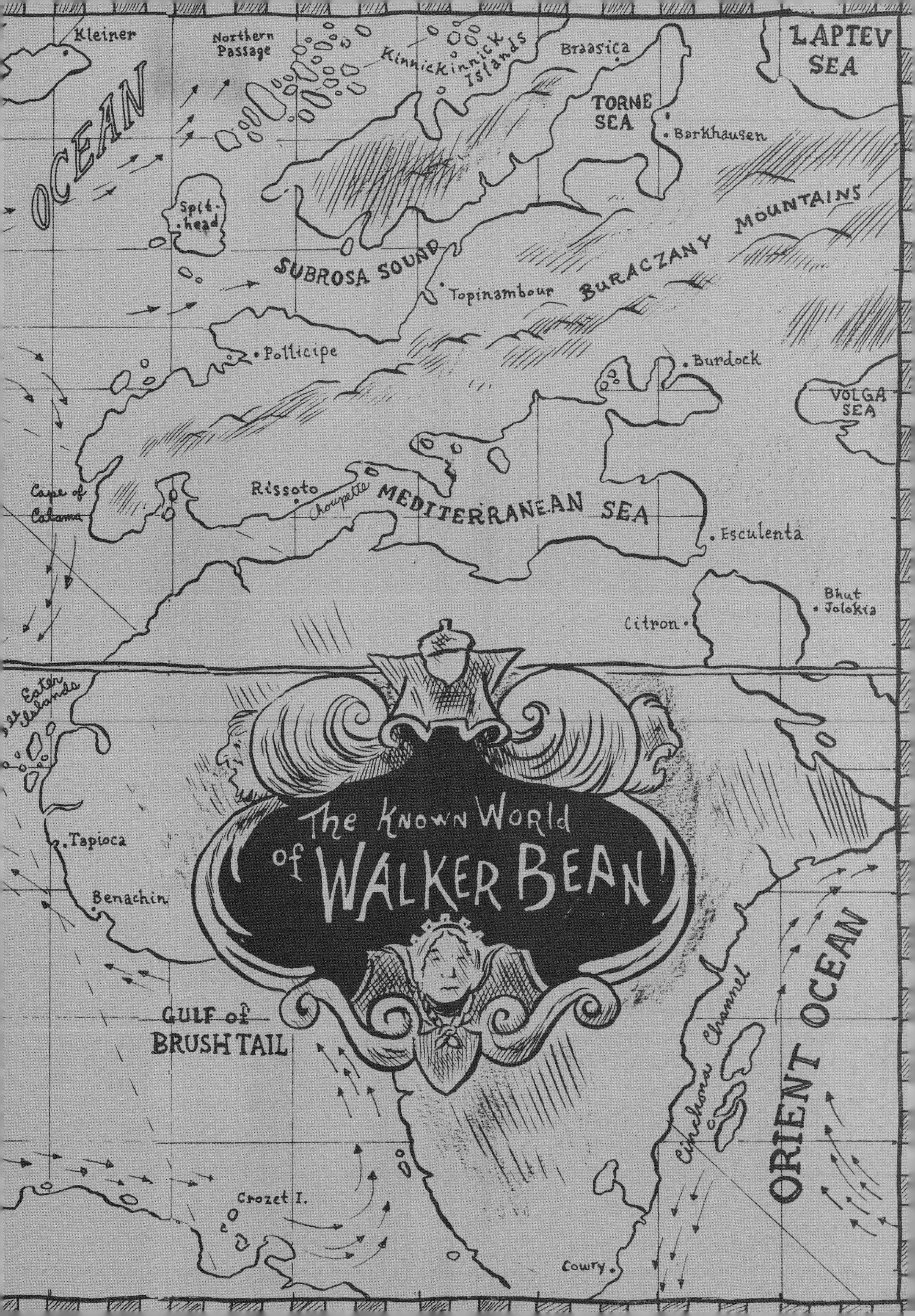

The Known World of Walker Bean
Kleiner
Northern Passage
Kinnickinnick Islands
Braasica
LAPTEV SEA
OCEAN
TORNE SEA
Barkhausen
Spit-head
BURACZANY MOUNTAINS
SUBROSA SOUND
Topinambour
Pollicipe
Burdock
VOLGA SEA
Cape of Calama
Rissoto
Choupette
MEDITERRANEAN SEA
Esculenta
Bhut Jolokia
Citron
Tapioca
Benachin
GULF of BRUSH TAIL
Cinchona Channel
ORIENT OCEAN
Crozet I.
Cowry

:01

First Second
New York

Copyright © 2010 by Aaron Renier

Published by First Second
First Second is an imprint of Roaring Brook Press,
a division of Holtzbrinck Publishing Holdings Limited Partnership,
175 Fifth Avenue, New York, NY 10010

Distributed in the United Kingdom by Macmillan Children's Books,
a division of Pan Macmillan.

Interior design by Aaron Renier and Colleen AF Venable

Colored by Alec Longstreth

Cataloging-in-Publication Data is on file at the Library of Congress.

ISBN: 978-1-59643-453-0

First Second books are available for special promotions and premiums
For details, contact: Director of Special Markets, Holtzbrinck Publishers.

First Edition September 2010
Printed in China
by RR Donnelley Asia Printing Solutions Ltd.,
Dongguan City, Guangdong Province
9 10

THE UNSINKABLE Walker Bean

Written and illustrated by Aaron Renier

Colored by Alec Longstreth

First Second

New York & London

With love to my mom.

For not only putting up with my nonsense,
but for taking it seriously.

For hundreds of years, from seaport to shantytown, a legend has been told to the children there....

The entire city of Atlantis... GONE!

... DESTROYED! By two BEASTS!

THOUSANDS of people... SNUFFED! Families torn apart FOREVER.

The beasts were captured by a small surviving fleet of ships...

...'n'sentenced to live the rest of their lives in an UNDER-WATER PRISON!

Somewhere, in the middle of the ocean... off the coast of an uncharted island chain...

...there is a TRENCH.

...FOR MILES IT DIVES BENEATH THE OCEAN'S FLOOR...

...PAST SMOKE-STACKS...SPEWING BOILING, TOXIC SULFUR...

...HERE, WHERE SUNLIGHT CANNOT REACH...

HERE, LIVE THE STRANGEST OF THE STRANGE.

CHOMP!

MNCH
MNCH
MNCH
MNCH
MNCH
MNCH
MNCH

HERE, LIVE THE MOST EVIL OF THE EVIL

SNAP!

HERE, IN THE DEEPEST, DARKEST SPOT, THE VERY BOTTOM OF THE OCEAN, DWELL TARTESSA AND REMORA, THE EVIL MERWITCH SISTERS.

3

SLOWLY, IN THEIR PITCH BLACK CELL, THEY BEGAN TO LOSE THEIR POWERS, WHICH DRIPPED OUT OF THEM LIKE *SILVERY GLOWING MOLASSES.*

DESPERATE TO HOLD ON, *THEY DEVISED A PLAN.* THEY SCOOPED UP THE REMAINS OF THEIR ENEMIES.

AND LIKE AN OYSTER FORMS A PEARL, THEY SWISHED THE SKULLS AND BONES IN THEIR *THICK, NACRE SALIVA...*

And when they were coated and transformed into magical bone-shaped pearls...

...they SPAT them onto the seabed.

PTOO!

PLNK!

And then stacked them up like a brick wall...

5

EACH ENCHANTED SKELETON REFLECTED
THE SECRETS OF ITS FORMER LIFE.
THE PAST, PRESENT, AND FUTURE
LAID OUT BEFORE THE SISTERS.

Even now... they can see us.

The visions from the wall are so STRONG that only those with HEART and BLOOD as THICK as theirs can gaze into it without going into SHOCK and DYING.

But what would be the price to pay to look into just ONE bone? A SNIFFLE? A COUGH? I'd risk that, to possibly get any answers to my long list of questions.

Yeah...

The location of John Rackham's treasure, the hidden cave on Mount Nebo... El Dorado!

ATLANTIS!

Now I know we're related for sure! I'll see you when I get back from Panapén, Bucko.

Have a safe trip, Grandpa.

Aye-aye! G'night!

'Night!

Thicker than Thieves

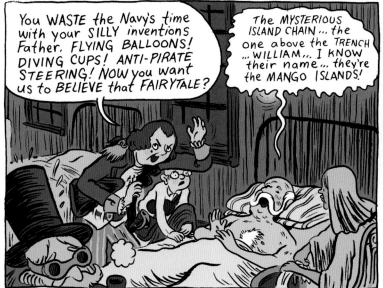

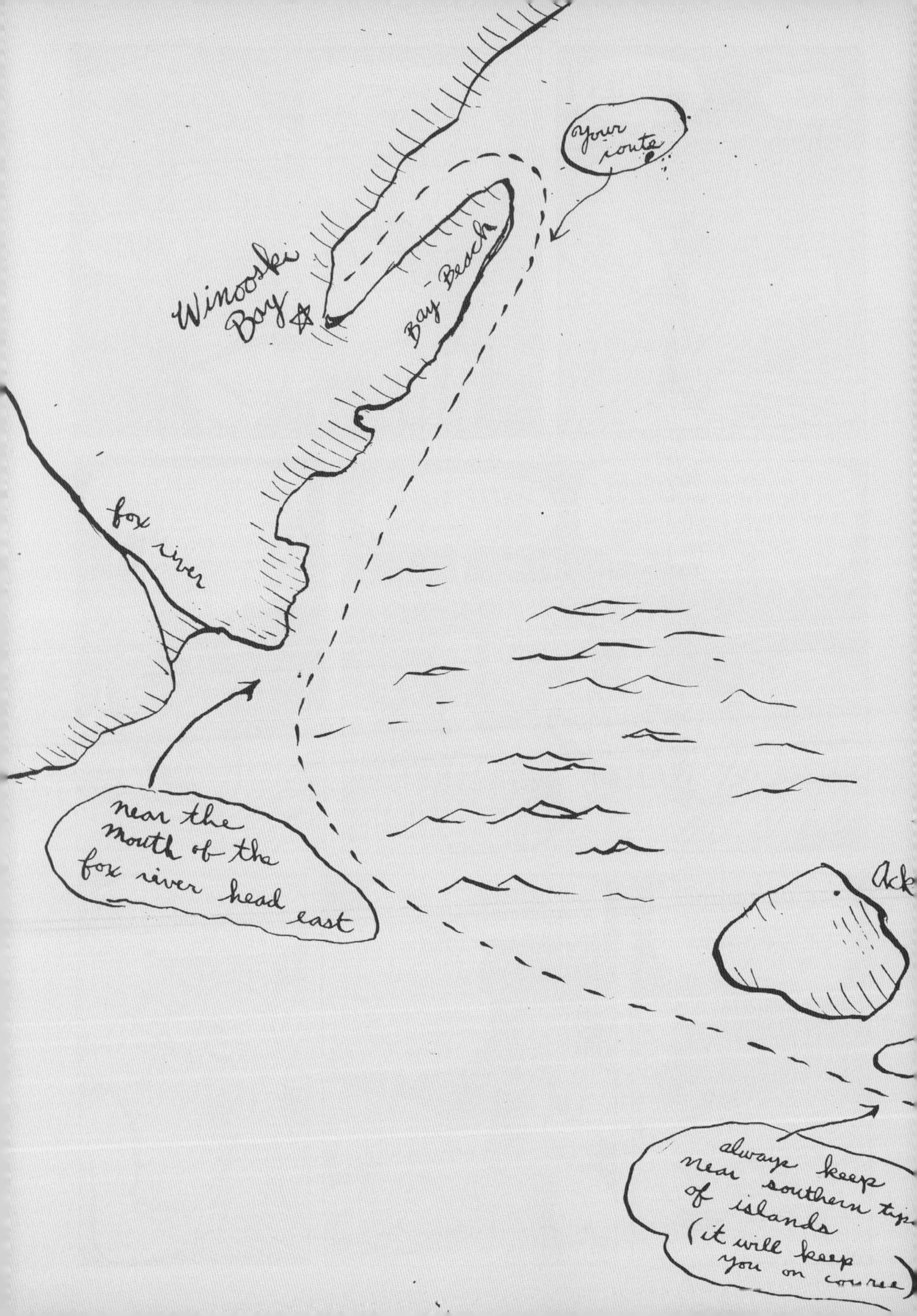

Your route

Winooski
Bay

Bay Beach

fox river

near the
mouth of the
fox river head east

Ack

always keep
near southern tip
of islands
(it will keep
you on course

N

the Mango
Islands

Cherimoya

Mango

Edesa
the tiny

Crescent

Plumb
Rock

aim to go between
Mango and Crescent

I... I...

I don't... I don't understand... you... you think they're REAL?

I KNOW they are... I SAW them, Walker...

Each morning in Panapén, I'd walk the docks, drink coffee, and check out the woodwork on luggers and brigs. And then...

Dear GOD.

...smashed... SMASHED to PIECES...

HUGE LOBSTER WOMEN! I rescued a man from them... and they SMASHED my boat and flung him back to sea! He drowned for sure! Worst night of my life!

LOBSTER women?

Then, the sun came... and my wreck drifted and smashed into this pier! I have NO WAY of repairing! I need to sell what I have. Maybe I can buy a DINGHY!!

And that's when I heard a voice...

Look around! Many valuable antiques! Beautiful scrimshaw!

Buy ME.

What is that there?

The strange man had it. It gives me the WILLIES... sell it to you cheap!

I didn't need to ask... I knew... I could FEEL it.

BUY ME...

I raced back to my cabin, and went to my journal.

open the bag...

"Only those with blood and heart as thick as theirs, may gaze into the bones." Hmm... is there any way to thicken my blood?

You're a HEARTY man, Mr. BEAN... surely you're MAN enough to PEEK...

I knew I shouldn't... But curiosity overcame me... as we left port...

YES... YES...

In the bottom drawer of my rolltop desk... there's a box I made for you... for your first voyage... keep it with you... It'll keep you safe.

Okay.

Remember what I always say... "You can create the stars in the sky..."

"...and move the mountains and the seas..." I remember. GOOD BYE!

Write me!

Snnfl!

"Write me?" From the middle of the OCEAN? That's impossi-

Was the person hopping on two feet? A strange limp?

They seem to lead ...right...to...

My HOUSE!?

Not a worry, men...

I'm not about to throw our FORTUNE into the ABYSS!

...BUT, we are going to make a TEENY "PIT-STOP" ...near the Mango Islands...

HWHAT??

To clear my CONSCIENCE! We'll just swing down there, eat some mangoes and kiwis ...like that STUPID song...

This is NOT what you AGREED to!

≥HIC≤

Then we'll turn back north! Up to the Laptev, and meet up with your acquaintance...

≥HIC≤ Yer FILTHY ≥HIC≤ RICH ONE!

That's an added TWO WEEK trip!

Believe me... I'm in this for the money! But if I ignore ANOTHER direct order from the ADMIRAL ...well... I'll be COURT-MARTIALED for SURE!

HOOEY-MANURE! Yer going to chase FIGMENTS of a sick man's IMAGINATION?!

If you're suggesting I believe that SILLY STORY, You're WRONG! I'm seeing this as an impromptu VACATION!

≥HIC!≤ But...what if when we ≥HIC≤ get there...them two BEASTS are REAL? 'N'they ATTACK?

I suppose I should have a plan for every "WHAT IF"... eh, Mr. Spittoon? Well... if we see those WATERY WENCHES I'll pretend to toss it back to them...

Grrrr...

Sniff Sniff

Then...when they least expect it...

23

Father's abandoned water tower project! A monolithic memorial to his CLAPTRAP!

WE KNOW YOU'RE UP THERE, BOY!!

You go that way, Bidet. We'll corner him.

AYE!

He's not this way!

WHAT THE??

He must've jumped into the trees!

H...hello?

HAHAHAHAHA

HUH!?

Wh...who's there?

LOOK INSIDE the BAG, you FAT, WEAK little boy!

I... I can't.

YESSS... YOU'VE BEEN WARNED...

In that case...

Let me introduce MYSELF. Heheheh...

No!... that's okay...

HAHAHA

SZZZZLLL

HAHAHAHAHAHAHAHAHAHAHAHA

POP

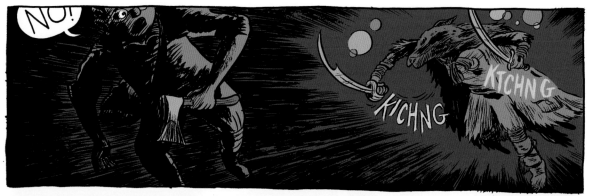

YES? YES? CAN'T YOU SEE I'M BUSY?

YER DAMP SQUIB!

AHHH! I Knew you'd come through, Doc! I'll reward you when we go south. A basket of TROPICAL FRUITS and CHEESES!

Don't bother... I only eat RAW sea food. Access to yer BAIT 'n' CHUM will suffice!

ARGH!

What? Um...

AH! YES! MY THICKSET THIEF! Where's the BAG? TELL ME!

BAG?

She... she TOOK it. THEY STOLE IT!

EEP!

HWAA?

NEW PLAN! NEW PLAN!

Let's see, LET'S SEE!

BIDET! THE WHITE FLAG!!!! SURRENDER? NOW? WHY?

THEY HAVE THE SKULL!

We'll BLOW them out of the water AFTER we get it back!

This's Captain William H. Bean, of the Ticonderoga! I'd like to CONVERSE with your CAPTAIN!

WISH GRANTED, BILLY BEAN! Th'name's KODIAK. Cap'n of the JACKLIGHT.

Yes... Mr.,, KODIAK... some of the "booty" you recently... um... "looted" from us is ... very... IMPORTANT to us.

HAR! HAR! You want back yer FRIPPERY?

HA HA HAHA HA

WHAT?!? Nononono! KEEP it! We've been meaning to switch to PAPER MONEY, and PLEASE, DON'T WORRY about our buildings! THEY NEEDED NEW SIDING! But the BAG... with a SKULL in it...

GRR...

THAT was yer PLAN? TO ASK THEM FOR IT? I SHOULDA KNOWN A HALFWIT COULD NEVER DO A JOB FOR ME!

WHAT??

Are you SUGGESTING YOU are IN CHARGE HERE?! MR. SPITTOON! LOCK THIS MAN IN THE-

Sir! Sir! They're ARMING th' CAN-

THMP

Shiv?

=Sigh=

Aren't you coming up? Nettle boiled some whitefish...and I'm going to borrow some instruments...

Her!

Another kegger?

Yeah, another party, Shiv. We finally have reason to CELEBRATE!

Yeah? Oh... I thought we still needed to gather ingredients for the BLOOD SOUP?

And aren't we being FOLLOWED by _Tarte-

Shhh!

You know better than ANYBODY, Shiv... the ocean has many ears...

SLAM

If they're out there...yes... they're following us... but if they are out there... then what we hope to see in the skull is also out there...

I truly hope we're being followed.

The SKULL!

OH NO!

PLP

44

What're you ROLLING in?

SHFL SHFL

≈Sigh≈ You REALLY need to clean, Shiv. It's FILTHY down here...

I really NEED to do THIS and THAT... yes ... I KNOW... THANKS.

SNF SNF SNF

Okay... just STOP for a second. I know this's all a bit... overwhelming... but please... let me help.

I'll do it LATER, Gen. I'm kinda busy now.

I know you're busy with your music... and you're worried about the stew... and bein' followed... but I really have a good feeling about everything. Like the sort of feeling I had about YOU... and WINOOSKI BAY... Okay? So... Relax.

≈Sigh≈

Please, come up to the party. I know they're not your sort of people... but you need to try a little harder... A.J. would love to help with your ideas.

Ugh!

Okay? You come up, and I'll pump out this STANK sitting water for you. And I can even-

No! That's enough, really... I'll come.

I'll be up in a few minutes.

Okay... c'mon Perrogi! TREAT!

...

SH

45

47

48

Dear Grandpa,

What can I say in a letter that I'll never send?

That I'm lost?...

...That I'm horribly scared. I'm failing you? That I might already be too late?

Oh, Grandpa

...I miss you so, so much.

...For the last few weeks I've been digging and organizing trash...

Why do you have all this... GARBAGE?

I don't believe in garbage.

I'm going to use this stuff to build my dad's forty piece self-playing orchestra... his "Automelodia".

Automelo-Wha?

...It's this machine Shiv's dad dreamt about making. One device that could play forty intruments on it's own...

Think of it! While the woodwinds go ♪LA-LI-LI-LA♪, the percussion'll go ♪Bibiddy-bip-bippity BOP!♪, you know?

Wha?

His father built and played musical instruments. Shiv helped string the violas.

We worked really well together...

One day Shiv and his parents were invited to Coloa, to help build a music ensemble.

When out of nowhere, a strange storm appeared...

NO!

NO!!!

GLP

... Genoa later rescued him from the water. I guess she saw him drowning in a dream.

ZZZ

SK SK SK

SCRTCH SCRTCH

And Sh—

SK SK SK

?

GRRRR

AAAGH!
BWOOF!

It's...
It's

BNK

OOH!

What's wrong with you?

I saw something ...a CREATURE. What'd you hit me with? A harmonica?

A rat ... you saw a rat.

No... it was BIG... with these EYES ... and these ... HANDS...

Yeah... a RAT... go to SLEEP...

... the sounds of the creaky boat eventually got my mind off the creature, and I could finally fall asleep.

ZZZZ

ZZZ

For the next couple days... as we got closer to Spithead, I had many near misses with the pirates. They'd come down through the hold to the cellar for beer... or to harass Shiv.

THMP

BWOOF BWOOF BWOOF!

No... you're leaving soon...

...I'm with her for life.

Besides... I still want to see inside the mystery box.

oh yeah!

What's that? Why're you crying?

That's what kept me afloat! He built it to be AIRTIGHT... it's a FLOTATION device.

KSSSHHH

KSSSH

Whoa.

KSSSHH

KSSSH

It... it can't be...

What? What can't they be?

They're the two possessions of this girl... from this song my grandpa likes... Leechi Boura.

HAHAHA! ♪ Like a bolt of lightning! ♪ Across the Shiny Sea! ♪ A return message for Leechi came from her family. ♪

Exactly! This is the message jug her family sent... and this is the star globe she found her way to the water with.

Whatever. Now you're pulling MY leg... How would you know what they LOOK like?

Good girl, good girl.

THMP

BWOOG WOOG WOOG

I brought you some bread and soup... and I threw the jug into the water around noon... like you said.

Thanks... thanks.

Then what? Did it ZIP off? Did it move in the water?

I don't know, Bean. I was mending a sail and threw it over my shoulder. I heard it hit the water...but when I looked, it was gone.

SNF SNF

≥Sigh≤

Now that jug is at the bottom of the ocean... how could I be SO STUPID to ask you to toss it away? He'll never see my letter.

Hey...

I'm on dog watch all night alone... if you want to come up and see the ship, tonight's the night. Fresh air'll do you good.

W-what about the crew?

MNCH MNCH

Something is wrong with the Captain. Genoa's called together a meeting. They'll be in the galley until they go to sleep.

C'mon... put this on... it's cold...

All right... if you're sure this is safe.

In this coat they'll think you're one of them.

MNCH MNCH

56

Just... calm... down....

Calm down? The captain's SICK! You want him to DIE?

Genoa... all this does is give us HOPE.

HOPE?

Uh...

Ahhh... FRESH AIR!

Um... Yeah...

W-wha...what's that?

What's what? Oh... it's a lemon tree. Gen has a small vegetable garden up on the beakhead.

I help her weed, but she does most of the work. Nettle makes a MEAN lemonade... to prevent scurvy. HMMM... I really need to get Gen to plant some sugar cane... or stevia.

You wanna see it, huh?

Yes... very much.

C'mon... let's keep walking.

Okay. So...the hammock, do you take naps there?

Naps? That's where Genoa stays. She says the sea air helps her sleep. Shoot! I forgot something. Stay here for a sec.

WHA?? WAIT...

Uh...

Mr. Saag! PLEASE LISTEN! I made a MISTAKE!

Kodiak said the sisters are HUNTING US! Let's RETURN it!

HUNTING US? NEVER!

You see... I've heard a VARIATION on the ol' tale. I heard the two sisters weren't always two HULKING BEASTS!

Once upon a time, they were the prettiest, most LUSCIOUS mermaids in the seven seas.

...AND THEY KNEW IT.

BUT THEY WERE BITTER AND JEALOUS OF THEIR ONLY RIVAL, NEPTUNE'S KINGDOM, THE BEAUTIFUL CITY OF ATLANTIS.

So the two devised a series of horrible events! BETRAYAL! POISONINGS! MURDERS!

ERUPTIONS! FIRES!

EARTHQUAKES! TSUNAMIS!

AN ENTIRE CIVILIZATION, AN ENTIRE HISTORY, LOST FOREVER!

The sisters fled, but were captured by Neptune's last surviving naval fleet.

Deep in the trench, a battle was fought.

Neptune and his army, DEAD.

THE SISTERS HUDDLED TOGETHER IN THEIR DEEP, DARK PRISON, ON A BED OF CADAVERS.

61

IN THE TOXIC WATERS, THEIR SKIN BLOATED, AND INFLATED WITH MILES AND MILES OF GUTS.

THEIR HANDS MELTED, TWISTED, AND CURLED INTO CLAWS.

THEIR BODIES MIRRORED THEIR SOULS... ROTTEN! ASHAMED BY THEIR UGLINESS, THEY HID...

... AND IN THE SHADOWS THEIR BODIES ADAPTED TO A WORLD WITHOUT ANY LIGHT!

They're NOT following us, because they CAN'T follow us. They can't face the world as the monsters they've become.

And even if they DID surface, they can't function in a world with SUNLIGHT anymore! They'd FREEZE UP! THEY'D BE PETRIFIED STIFF! HAHAHAHA!!!

Kodiak was a FOOL to look into it! But he PROVED the skull is AUTHENTIC! All we can do is continue to Spithead... gather ingredients...

... and make the blood thickening soup.

Then, we'll all eat up! And TOGETHER gaze into its TROVE of SECRETS!

Hehehehe

THE RICHES'N' TREASURES OF ATLANTIS WILL BE OURS!

HUH!

HEAR! HEAR!

CLINK

POWDER MONKEY!

You come in here fer STORYTIME?? Who's on WATCH? Yer DOG?

Buuu

ANSWER ME, MONKEY!

...

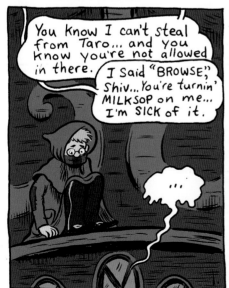

You OKAY?

I...I...

Sorry I left you hangin'... she wouldn't shut up...

He...he doesn't know I have it.

Bean?

Yeah? Yeah ...I'm fine.

Stay close.

Yeah...

71

SHIV!

TARO!

WHOA-HO-HO! PERROGI!

So many KISSES for me!

She's happy to see you!

I'm happy to see you too! You're so skinny, though... doesn't Nettle feed you? Here, let me. Please! Finish my breakfast!

I'm so full! Please! Help me out! Your friend too!

Thanks! Hey, Walker! You want a pork bun?

MNCH MNCH MNCH

Walker?

♫ BEAN ♫

This is sooooo much more entertaining than that stuffy Captain's quarters.

Um....

Hope ta see ya again soon!

You KNOW that guy?

Um...
Heh...

Taro Tung, meet Walker Bean.

H-hello.

Pleased to meet you... NOW... what can I do you for?

Well... I'd like thirty yards of harp string...

And, Walker'd like to get a boat ride home.

Coming right up!

?

WHOA.

Um... Mr. Tung?

Call me Taro!

Yes, Taro... what's that tablet?

Oh, an old alphabet of sorts. No living generation speaks it. Pretty useless.

I've seen it before... See? My grandpa drew a picture of it.

Ah, yes! That's it!

How much is it?

You can find useless stuff on the street for FREE.

I know.... but this would make a nice "get-well" gift.

It's yours, Mr. Bean! It's been in here longer than I have! PLEASE!

REALLY? Thank you SO MUCH!

Now... where is home?

Winooski Bay.

Well...

Ahhh! Fur trading country! I know some traders in the north docks that sail there. I will introduce you.

I don't... I don't want to go home, Mr. Tung... Taro.

What? WHY? Why'd we come here? No offense, Taro.

None taken.

I... I want to go to the Mango Islands.

....

You... you TOOK IT? I..., I DON'T BELIEVE IT. Even after I TOLD you what THEY'D DO TO ME? I'm trying to HELP YOU and you DO THIS TO ME?!!?

EN GARDE!

GIVE IT BACK! NOW!

No! LISTEN TO ME, SHIV!

FIGHT!

I TRUSTED YOU!!!

SHIV! PLEASE! LISTEN TO ME!

76

As ENTERTAINING as this is... could you remind her that I'm FRAGILE?!

HRG

STOP!!!

STOP! YOU'RE KILLING HIM!

POP

Hey...

...Walker...

...You awake?

uh....

Well, HELLO there!

Who do we got here?

A THIEF and his ACCOMPLICE!

Oh! Um! I'm SO SORRY. You reminded me of someone.

Who ARE YOU?! TALK!

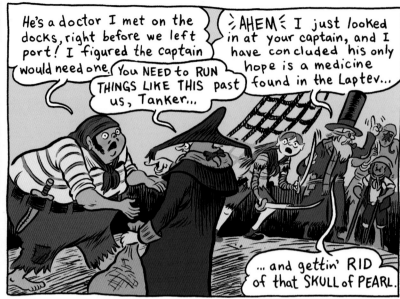

He's a doctor I met on the docks, right before we left port! I figured the captain would need one.

You NEED to RUN THINGS LIKE THIS past us, Tanker...

⸮AHEM⸮ I just looked in at your captain, and I have concluded his only hope is a medicine found in the Laptev...

...and gettin' RID of that SKULL of PEARL.

DON'T LISTEN TO HIM! HE KNOWS A RICH GUY UP THERE! HE WANTS TO SELL IT TO HIM!

GRRR...

As I was SAYING... if you want to save him you must take my advice! This SOUP you're making will offer a TEMPORARY relief, but it won't cure him, or protect the rest of you from that CURSED object.

He's a FAKE! There's something FISHY about him!

ENOUGH!

HUH!!!

TKTY
TKTY
TKTY
TKTY
TKTY

BE OFF WITH YA!

NO!

NOW... can we speak SENSIBLY without that RACKET?

HUH!

What? What sort of PIRATES are ya? That's what you do with THIEVES and MUTINEE AGH!!!

EEEEK!

85

93

ooo

oooh

;hack!

oooh...

;cough!

Hey.

Hey.

We need you two to get to work. Patches wanted you to shovel coal...but I got you on gutting detail. Besides... with Hamhock and Tanker shoveling we have the engine pumping full steam. I've never seen the Jacklight move this fast.

Thanks. So... where're we headed?

North... to the Laptev. Everyone seems to trust him now.

We don't.

Yeah... Neither do I.

Let's go! We have zero time to sit around.

Okay... I know... five minutes.

CHG CHG CHG CHG

You won't believe it... but I think I might have some ... news.

News?

Wow-a-wow... it came BACK! Does it still have your letter inside? Is it a new letter? OPEN IT!

Dearest Walker,
I'm so incredibly relieved you're alive.

After the battle in Winooski Bay, your father told me you were dead. I knew he was wrong.

IDIOT!

I have to say your plan to continue to the Mango Islands by yourself is...too dangerous. If you can get a trip home with or without the skull... it would make my days best.

Your father left with his new fleet. He should be near soon. I had to threaten him with a court-martial, because he didn't believe the letter was from you.

FOOLERY!

FOOL!

Sister Martha has been a great help. She found the jug in the harbor ... and has been looking after me. She baked some tiny cookies for you.

GINGER SNAPS!

SNF, SNF
SNF

I'm sorry my hand-writing is so shakey. Don't think it's only because of the sickness. I'm mostly giddy to hear from you. It gives me such hope in dreams. That we can create stars and move mountains.

MNCH
MNCH

You lucked out meeting Shiv. He sounds like a very creative boy. A good friend. If he's still with you, stay close to him.

MNCH MNCH

As for the drawing you sent me ... I believe that what you saw is a type of primate... an "Aye-aye." It's supposed to be a sign of bad luck... but it is most likely harmless. Strange it would be on the boat.

You saw an AYE-AYE?? On THIS ship?

When you hit me with yer HARMONICA.

No you didn't. It was a RAT. I REMEMBER.

≥Sigh≤

I'm very glad you decided to throw the jug into the ocean... I can imagine that would have been tough, not knowing it would make it to me... I didn't know if it would either. I'm so so happy it did. Be safe and get home in one piece. Write again soon.
Love,
Grandpa

Can she have a cookie?

SNF SNF SNF

Of course.

MNCH MNCH

SNF SNF SNF

Hey, Nettle. Where do you want these?

SHIV!

Here on the table is fine. Take a load off fer a bit.

Thanks.

I know you have fine intentions, Walker... but we'll be watching you.

Oh...

Um....

Just do your best in your new situation. It is a shame about your sick paps. Nothin' worse than a sick paps. If I could send him a batch of soup, I would.

Th- thanks.

Can we help cook? Chop anything?

No... help is on its way...

97

T-TNK

Stout... I need the beets, potatoes, celery, and cabbage chopped. Not too fine.

"STOUT?" He's a tiny METAL MAN?

CHP CHP CHP
CHP CHP
CHP

H-how does he w-work? Is he ALIVE?

I don't know really. Never really thought about it. He's always worked, ever since I was a little girl.

CHP CHP CHP.

Hey, Nettle... I got the rest of the ingredients from the garden. Tomatoes, onions, garlic... I even dried some thyme and...

CHP CHP CHP CHP
CHP CHP CHP CHP CHP
CHP CHP CHP CHP CHP
CHP CHP CHP CHP
CHP CHP CHP CHP
CHP CHP CHP

Oh.

If you're done with the meat, get up topside. There's a strong wind now, and we need the fore-sail braced. No time for CHIT-CHAT.

98

Well, we need to dump the guts in the chum bucket... and swab the deck.

FINE! WHATEVER! Just get up there! The sun'll be down in an hour!

So, did you look in on them?

They can barely sit up for water. I don't know how they'll EAT soup.

I've never seen Kodiak like this...

:Sigh:

The deck! It's SPOTLESS! Where's the...

MNCH!

SHLRP! SHLRP! SHLRP!

GHASP!

HUH!

BEAN! GET THIS GUY A NAPKIN! BLECH! HA!

MNCH!

MNCH!

I told you ... he's a DEMON.

And I agreed with you.

99

The soup is good.

Sure... but I'm still not looking into that skull.

I don't think anybody will, unless Kodiak or Avery get better.

Yeah...

...um...

So... I think I have a new plan to get to the Mango Islands.

Oh yeah?! What, you gonna build a GIANT catapult and fling yerself there?

I know I sound crazy. And believe me, the plan has its kinks... but if I could only find my book bag... and look at my grandpa's notes.

Genoa has it... in the garden. I was going to wait for her to hate me less, and then ask for it back.

Where's she now?

Well... thank you.

Yup.

So... how's the Captain? How's Mr. Avery?

Not so great, BEAN. Not so great.

Siiigh...

He's been in my life for so long. I've known him longer than anybody else on this boat.

I know that doctor is up to something... but if there is a medicine for him up north, then I'd do anything to get there.

Yeah.

I'm sorry about your grandpa. You're pretty close to him, huh?

Yes... very.

What about your mom and dad? Are they there for him?

No... my dad is probably looking for us...

Siiigh

... my mom died before I got to know her.

What about you?

What about me, what?

Where're your mom and dad?

Never knew them.

I dream a lot. I dreamt about finding Shiv, when he lost his family... I had one about you... and the skull... I had one about that witch following us... a bunch of others...

...but those that I really REMEMBER have this unique REALNESS to them. When I wake up I feel this ENERGY... and this SPARKLE... like it was a SIGN... a MARKER.

You want part of a lemon?

Um... I don't think they're very good for your teeth.

My FIST isn't very good for your teeth.

What?

Siiigh

Sorry... I'm trying really hard to not hate you... you know, for Shiv.

Oh... thanks.

So... why do you think only one of the witches is following us?

Well if one skull is that important, they really can't go and leave thousands unattended.

Oh... right.

We're going faster than the witch could ever go... and we're traveling both day and night. She only can move at night. By the time she finds that skull, we'll hopefully be long gone.

Yeah. Hey, there's the North star. We're on course.

You know the constellations?

A few.

Well, you see that "W" shape to the right?

Cassiopeia's Crown?

Yeah...

Every night on our trip, at around this time, Cassiopeia will be directly over the Laptev. That's exactly where we're headed.

Oh! Okay...

That's IT!

Dear Grandpa,

We're headed north under the command of that strange "doctor." After what happened on the steam engine, most everybody trusts his motives.

And now instead of saying he'd sell the skull to the man in the Laptev, he's telling the pirates they'll rob the man blind, after they get the medicine.

I think he'd change his story over and over depending on who was listening.

It's so cold now... I can always see my breath. Everyday we do nothing but hours of tedious work.

Mending, caulking, swabbing ... really boring stuff.

But at night it's completely different.

Shiv keeps them under control with his music, while I spend most nights camped out working on my two projects.

One is my first actual MACHINE without your help. I'm sending you the prototype plans on a separate sheet of paper.

And the second is my elaborate plan to turn the ship around.

I've been studying your drawing of "anti-pirate steering" and thinking of a way to use it.

rudder

steering pole

If I could just CUT the steering pole

And attach a SECRET steering pole in the hold. The helmsman would THINK he was steering... but really it would be me.

CLOSE-UP

SECRET STEERING POLE

HIS WOULDN'T WORK!

I could gently, without them noticing, turn the boat completely around!

In order to make them think we're headed north, I'd steal all their compasses...

...and then SURROUND the ship with coal blackened canvas to match and HIDE the real night sky.

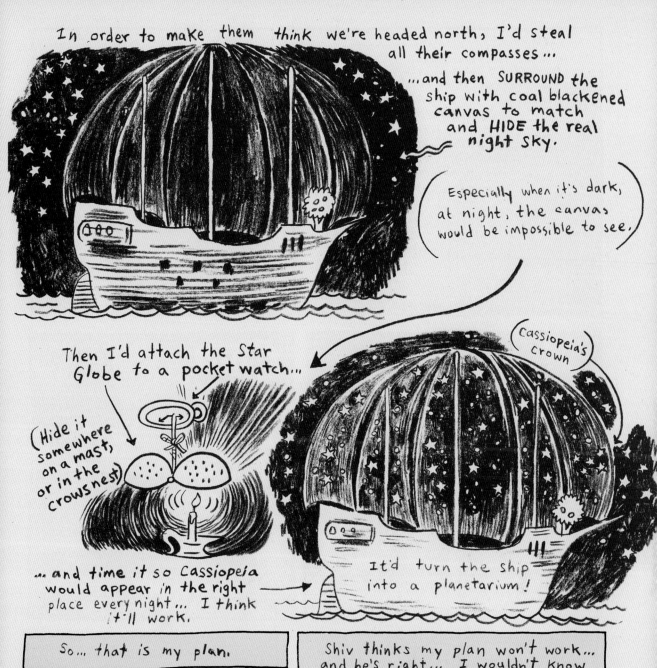

Especially when it's dark, at night, the canvas would be impossible to see.

Then I'd attach the Star Globe to a pocket watch...

(Hide it somewhere on a mast, or in the crows nest)

Cassiopeia's Crown

...and time it so Cassiopeia would appear in the right place every night... I think it'll work.

It'd turn the ship into a planetarium!

So... that is my plan.

I really think you should just build a catapult.

Shiv thinks my plan won't work... and he's right... I wouldn't know how to cut the steering pole so it could be reattached in the morning. It can't look like it's been tampered with.

Shiv says we're somewhere in the Northern Passage.

Those must be the Kinnickinnicks.

YELP!

The more and more I learn about Dr. Patches, the more I don't understand who he is. Yesterday he must've stepped on Perrogi's tail, and she bit his leg...

...but he didn't notice at all!

And, when he finally did...

MUTT!

NO! STOP!

WAK!

POW!

MONSTER!

HMM HMM

I really need to turn this boat around...

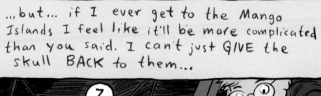

...but... if I ever get to the Mango Islands I feel like it'll be more complicated than you said. I can't just GIVE the skull BACK to them...

Z

ZZZ

After Saag said why they'd never leave the trench, to see one out in broad daylight changed everything for me.

Zzz

Why would they stay in hiding? What's stopping them from ruling the entire world?

I need to give it back to them... but I need to make sure they're never seen again...

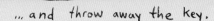

... and throw away the key.

Hello?

NETTLE!

Still hungry?

I wasn't going to eat it! It's not for me!

You don't need to eat in secret, Walker! I'm happy to beef you up! I'm glad you like my cooking!

Uhhh...

My my my! I got a jug JUST LIKE THAT! 'Cept mine has a dolphin on it. Very nice!

What're they lookin' at?

Uh...

There! Some strange lights!

Oh! Yeah!

HUH?

WHA??

115

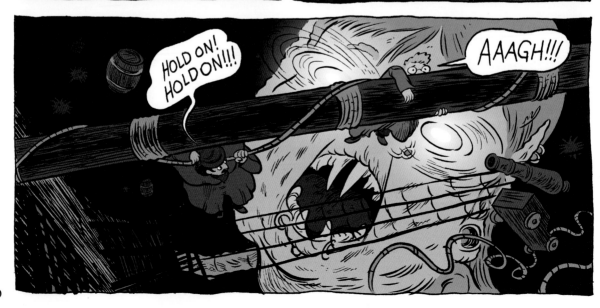

122

SAVED BY THE SUN!
I'll check on the Captain and Avery!

Oh no...

GEN?

Avery didn't make it. The Captain is alive... but he can't be moved.

ABANDON SHIP! We'll COMMANDEER another BOAT!

Did you not HEAR what I JUST SAID, "DOCTOR"? We need a different plan!

I KNOW! I have a plan! Where's my drawing?!?

:GLP:

Ahhh...

Yessss

I have a plan...

HEEE!

123

G-Genoa... she told me...

...She told me... he's a PLAGIARIST and a ⟩COUGH⟨ ⟩COUGH⟨ THIEF! He's NO DOCTOR... that's fer certain. If Genoa hadn't been force-feedin' me... I'd be gone.

Hang in there...

Hang in there.

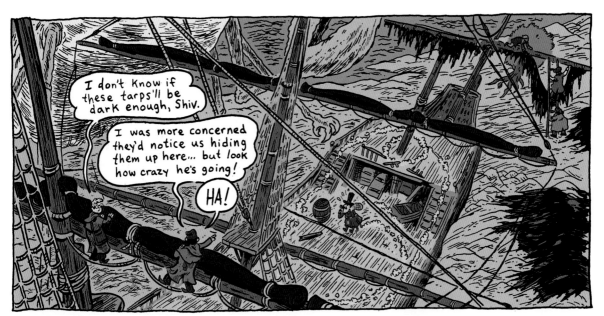

131

Nice work.

Thanks.

Sorry the garden was destroyed.

Me too. I repotted some...

...composted the rest.

WHA?

Have you seen this boy? He's SHORT... Kind of slow... PUDGY... blond?

He was KIDNAPPED by PIRATES!

No... Sorry...

UGH!

This is POINTLESS, Mr. Ottoman! I can't believe we're chasing a letter in a bottle! I mean, there's NO WAY a message in a bottle could get to the person it was written to in that short amount of time! It's RIDICULOUS!

I'd love a bottle like that.

WOULDN'T WE ALL! I don't have a WORD in my vocabulary to describe how RIDICULOUS that is!

"RIDICULOUS" is good, sir.

Well... did it look like his handwriting?

135

137

139

140

141

Totally.

It feels like just clear skies above us.

Now we only need to gather everybody's compas-

Here they come.

Thank you, Stout!

HA!

Cassiopeia's CROWN! Directly on course!

Your plans came with perfect timing. I've NEVER seen a ship moving this fast... When we arrive in the Laptev... you'll be... REIMBURSED.

HEE!

I have to be honest, Doc. I was gunna SLIT yer THROAT if this didn't work.

... SO GLAD yer PLEASED.

C'mon BEAN!

145

146

149

Everything is fine... we're headed north east.

Thanks for helping me replant these... it means a lot to me, Shiv.

Yup.

Are you not talking to me again?

No... I am... I just don't know what to say... I thought you didn't trust the doctor... yet you're following his plan...

Nobody else has ANY IDEA what to do, Shiv! I just want everything back to normal! I wish I NEVER stole the skull! I need Kodiak to be OKAY!

Gen...

Okay?

Yeah.

Hey...

I don't want him to go, Shiv. You and Kodiak. You're my family.

Hey... you want to know a secret?

Hmm?

Walker HAS another idea! Walker has a PLAN! These STARS! They're FAKE!

WHAT ARE YOU TALKING ABOUT?

I also know you were tryin' to see your mom in that skull. But you won't get what you want following that doctor. Walker has his head on straight.

It's ILLOGICAL!

They put up FAKE STARS!

≤COUGH≥ ≤COUGH≥ I know! This all reminds me of the gang back in Braasica! Makes me miss it!

You know what I always say..."trust yer gut"... besides... you can't trust the beast of a man that'd hit Perrogi.

Walker...

...where are we exactly?

Around... here. I'm pretty sure we'll collide with the Navy... and the witch, off the coast of the Mangoes... tomorrow night.

Um... sir...? the... sun...

YOU CAN'T BE SERIOUS!

I don't UNDERSTAND! I DON'T! WHERE ARE WE? And why is it getting so WARM?.'? WHY is this HAPPENING?!!

Someone! Give me a piece of paper! And a quill!

Maybe the witch is using her MAGICAL powers and altering the HEAVENS.

HORSE FEATHERS! She can't ALTER the—YOU!! YOU WERE ON WATCH! A SABOTEUR! GAG HIM! Toss him in with the BALLAST!

To STATIONS! NO MORE DILLY-DALLYING! From now on I'm steering! FULL SPEED AHEAD!!!

AND FROM NOW ON WE'RE ALL ON WATCH! NO SLEEP 'TIL WE'RE IN ARCTIC WATERS!

I'll brew some tea!

Tea?

Tea... to keep us AWAKE.

Yes... I was just suspicious of her scheming tone.

SO... obviously OUR idea to make soup... didn't work. YOU WERE RIGHT.

Arr... thank you.

But the reason I went on this voyage... was more than to get TREASURE... I... I wanted to find...

Atlantis.

YES! YES! YES! HAHA!

I mean... I'm ALL for ROBBING this rich man that you know... but does he know what you're bringing him? What is he CAPABLE of? WHO is this man?!

Have you ever heard of Thanatos the Tyrant? Aricin the Red? The Old Pirate Herringbone?

OF COURSE! They're ALL INSPIRATIONS to me! They all DIED searching for the lost city!

Yes... He's of their BLOOD. He's... RELATED to those men. If you FINALLY get us NORTH... I can see to it that you have an IN DEPTH conversation about the city of Atlantis.

Yes! Yes! I'll get us there!

Walker...

155

159

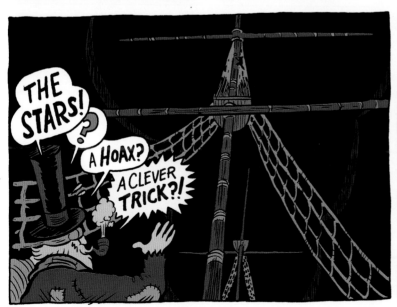

THE STARS!?

A HOAX?

A CLEVER TRICK?!

ALL HANDS ON DECK! EMERGENCY!!! TEAR DOWN THOSE SOILED TARPS!!!

BFM! BFM!

WHO'S FIRING!? I DIDN'T GIVE ANY ORDERS TO FIRE!

HUH!

?

GEN?!! BEAN?!!

?

WE HAVEN'T MEMORIZED THOSE YET, SHIV! WHAT ARE YOU SAYING???

HOLD FAST!

AAAGH!!

171

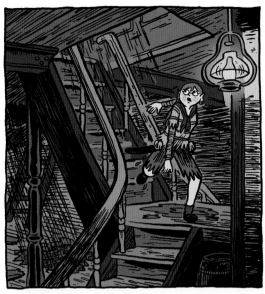

You okay? Did you see yer mom?

No... it didn't know about her.

What DID you see?

A lot, Bean.

I'll see you two back at the shore.

SPLP

I shouldn't have said anything.

How were you to know... HEY!

Walker! The NAVY!!! THEY'RE LEAVING!

NO!

HEY!

C'mon, Bean... they're gone. Let's go.

BOYS! BOYS!

Where... where's GENOA?!?

She's alive... she went for a swim, I guess.

Kodiak is... he's dead.

Wha?

No...

She... she already knew.

Nettle... where's my dad? Is he okay?

Yer dad? OH MY! That's RIGHT! Captain Bean is yer DAD!

I'm sorry, Walker... another Navy ship picked him up. They took Patches as a prisoner. As soon as that boat blew up, they raised their sails... and left.

He left me for dead... again?

I need to get back to the crew. If you see Stout, bring him to me. I need to boil some water!

Yes... okay.

Hello, Walker.

I didn't mean to startle you.

That's okay, A.J.

Quite a mess.

Uh-huh...

Found a small spring up past that grove of trees. The stream pours right into the Atlantic. I think that's where we'll have the funeral. At the mouth of the stream.

Oh...

Listen, nobody knows just how we ended up so far south... and Nettle and I won't say a thing.

Thank you.

You only did what you felt was right... you didn't kill Kodiak, and deep down Genoa knows that. We were all so set on looking into that skull, that we lost sight of where we were going.

I'm sure you won't hear this from anybody else... but your plans saved us... and I just wanted to say "thanks."

Dearest Walker,

It's like night and day. One second I was knocking on death's door, the next I was starving for rhubarb pie and a hot cup of coffee.

I don't know how you did it. If your plan worked the way you hoped... but something worked.

I pray this message finds you as well as I am. There is so much to respond to since your last letter. I'll keep this short so I can get this to you.

A metal teapot man! The tablet from my drawing! A Merwitch! Your plans to give the Irma wheels! Your mobile planetarium!

I suspect the metal on those objects is called "Orichalcum." In my readings on Atlantis it was said to be used in everything... but now that you say it's a power source... well, now I want to reread those old texts with that knowledge.

"Stout" sounds fantastic! I hope to meet him someday.

My first order of business now is to start constructing the wheels for the Irma. I am going to add some rubber to them though. I imagine it being a jolting ride.

Tell me about it.

When I told you a million times that you can create the stars in the sky and move mountains and the sea... I didn't ever think you'd be so... _Literal._ You make me so proud.

I couldn't eat the soup, but Sister Martha said it was very... interesting. The thing the pirates don't understand is that when the story says you can look into the skull if your "heart and blood are as thick as theirs," it doesn't mean you can just thicken your blood and look into it...

It means basically the same thing as the saying "blood is thicker than water." It means you can only look into it if you are of the same blood. If you're related to them.

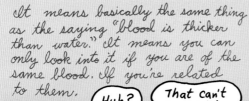

Huh?

That can't be right...

Have you shown Shiv the "automelodia" you've been working on? Even if it's just a prototype, I'm sure he'd be _thrilled_ to see it! I know I am!

WAIT.

WHAT?

Sigh

I hope to see you very soon!
Love,
Grandpa

What's he talkin' about?!

Calm down.... it's not even CLOSE to being done.

Let me see! PLEASE!

189

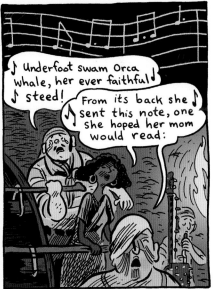

191

ACKNOWLEDGMENTS

For trust and guidance: Janna Morishima, Steven Malk, Mark Siegel, Calista Brill, Alec Longstreth, Craig Thompson, Brett Warnock, Colleen Venable, Chris Staros, Laura Park, Sam Carbaugh, Jeff Smith, Sheila & Dave, and last, but hardly least, David Coyle for the music composition.

For inspiration, life, and love: My family, Beluga, Daniel, Grandpa Koch, Gina, Lauren, Nate, Gabrielle, Matt & Truen (pssst... Hi, Axel!), Paul, Shiren, Liz, Kaz, Greig, Carson, Austin, Karen, Jon, Julia, Alex, Tom, Sarah, Daria, Evelyn, Jeff, Jen, Brian, Alison, Nate, Jeremy, Corinne, Ezra, Grant, Kazu, Claudia, Uncle Jerry, Kollodi, Philipos, all the people who enjoyed *Spiral-Bound*, and to all my great friends in New York, Portland, Milwaukee, and Chicago.

And an ecstatic welcome to the world to Soleia Ray!

The adventure continues in

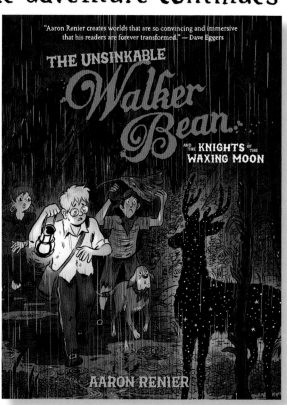

Early Sketches
of book #2

wheel add-on to patches cart

riding barefoot

the ORIGINAL SCREW

Hole to Jungle

Cave with a thicket roof

WALKER BEAN
preliminary doodles & ideas

SHIV   WALKER BEAN

the unsinkable

WALKER BEAN

My first drawing of Walker & Sh

a.J.

Hamhock

Nettle

Saag

outside

Huge old Map
the world

tons of
books
artifacts

well... pr
Fr

walker
and historians

grandpa's
desk

larg
"Qui
sen
to
by
g'

IRMA

Inside the Water Tower

↑
Workbench

strange half
finished ship

Stove

ABOUT THE CARTOONIST

AARON RENIER was born and raised in Green Bay, Wisconsin. He has been drawing comics, in one way or another, for as long as he can remember. His illustrations have appeared in a wide variety of places, including the exterior of an entire city bus, making it look like an aquarium. He won the Eisner award for cartoonist deserving wider recognition for his first graphic novel, *Spiral-Bound*. He is the illustrator of a series of books about the Knights of the Roundtable by Gerald Morris, and a picture book by Alice Shertle titled *An Anaconda Ate My Homework*. This book was drawn in Brooklyn, New York and Chicago, Illinois, between trips to various parks and lagoons with his trusty hound, Beluga.

ABOUT THE COLORIST

ALEC LONGSTRETH was born and raised in Seattle, Washington. In 2002 he graduated from Oberlin College, where he majored in technical theater and in 2007 he graduated with highest honors from Pratt Institute, where he majored in illustration. After living in many different cities around the country, Alec now resides in White River Junction, Vermont, where he teaches at the Center for Cartoon Studies, self-publishes his comic book *Phase 7*, and works as a freelance illustrator and colorist.

ABOUT THE BOOK

The art was drawn on Strathmore vellum bristol board, with a standard yellow #2 pencil. It was then inked on with a Pentel Brush Pen, Rapidograph pen, and fountain pen. Words were lettered with a Micron 08 felt tip pen. After it was inked and pencil lines erased, some pages were scratched and ripped with razor blades to make rain and splashes. Wite-Out with a foam applicator was also used to make white shapes, and black colored pencils were used to draw Walker's illustrations. In Aaron's opinion, the tooth of the paper combined with the brush pen make really nice flowing organic lines, the variety of pens allows better control, and the colored pencil, razor, and Wite-Out add fun textures. The colors of this book were applied using Photoshop CS3, an iMac, and a Wacom drawing tablet. After drawing and inking, each page was scanned into the computer. The colors were added to the file on a series of layers underneath the drawing (sort of like an old animation cell). Using some old, faded children's books for inspiration, Aaron and Alec created a custom palette of 75 colors, which are the only colors used in this book. Coloring a big book is easier when one has only a limited number of colors to choose from, and it makes the colors feel very unified.